SHORT
TALL
Tales to Tell
Selected from Tiny Tall Tales

by Ennis Rees

Illustrated by Quentin Blake

SCHOLASTIC BOOK SERVICES
NEW YORK • TORONTO • LONDON • AUCKLAND • SYDNEY

Copyright © 1967 by Ennis Rees. This abridged edition is published by Scholastic Book Services, a division of Scholastic Magazines, Inc., by arrangement with Abelard-Schuman Limited.

1st printing .... February 1974
Printed in the U. S. A.

Texas Tall Tales

A man in Texas is so big
  He makes a taxi stall.
So the driver has to make two trips
  In order to take him all.

X

There's a fellow in Texas who is so rich
  His life is like a dream.
He lights his fires with hundred-dollar bills
  And skates upon ice cream.

The bears in Texas have learned to ride,
   And now they really put up a battle.
They'll knock a cowboy from his horse
   And rope him from the saddle.

They had a wind in Texas
   That blew so hard and high
It kept the sun from setting
   And blew the moon from the sky.

Big Rains

It rains so hard on the tropic isle
   Of Solong-Solong in the Sulu Sea
That the sky is as wet as the River Nile
   And the monkeys swim from tree to tree.

It rains so hard in Florida
   Birds swim instead of fly,
And the fish swim up through the falling flood
   Until they are high in the sky.

Lucky Escapes

Caught at the top of a burning building,
    The famous Mr. I. Rather
Found himself some soap and water
    And came down on the lather.

A lady fell into the sea
    And up from the deep and dark
Came an ugly fin, but luckily
    It was a *man*-eating shark!

Sneezes, Snores
and Coughs

Jack and Willie of New Orleans
   Are very lazy boys.
To sneeze, Jack tosses back his head,
   Then Willie makes the noise.

There's a fellow in Philadelphia
   Whose snores are so house-shaking
He has to sleep three blocks away
   To keep himself from waking.

Granny Goodgrit had a cough
So echoaciously loud
It broke the windows in the house
And blew away a cloud.

They say there's a man by the name of Joe
   Who is so very skinny
He doesn't even have a shadow.
   At least you can't see any.

Blinkey Bluejohn was so tall
   He never could have told
If he were standing in a fire
   Or if his feet were cold.

There's a man so tall in Colorado
   That when he wants to shave
He has to climb to the top of a ladder.
   They call him Daring Dave.

Peculiar People

There's a man in Mobile whose mouth is so large
    That he has a very strange fear.
He is, in fact, afraid to laugh,
    For his head might disappear.

There's a man in Massachusetts
So strict and so upright
It's all they can do to get him to
Lie down and sleep at night.

There's a man in Miami who walks so slow
   He always wears spurs with sharp little wheels.
He says he wears them to keep his shadow
   From stepping on his heels.

His younger sister lives so fast
   She's now a year older than her brother.
In fact, if she can manage to last,
   She'll soon be as old as her mother.

When Florinda Fury went to town
She always wore a bear-skin gown,
And when she wanted to look her best,
For a hat she'd wear an eagle's nest.

One man was so ugly he didn't dare pass
In front of a mirror, for sadly
A careless glance would shatter the glass
And also scare him badly.

Howling Mad Brown had such a hot temper
That even the shirt he wore
Would very often burn to ashes
And sift upon the floor.

Sally is so extremely modest
She always wears glasses — and why?
To keep her from looking at anything
With her naked eye.

There's a man in Montana who is so big
That though it gives him a cough
He always takes off his hat outdoors
So the clouds won't knock it off.

This same fellow, when he was a boy,
　　Would bump his head on a limb,
For he grew so fast that even his shadow
　　Could not keep up with him.

Now, if he stands on a tall enough chair,
　　He can button his collar with ease,
But to put his hands in his pockets at all
　　He has to get down on his knees.

Little Mary
Is so small
It takes three people
To see her at all.

So Long That . . .

"My steamboat is so enormously long,"
    The captain told his friends,
"That it's fitted with hinges every half mile
    To help it get round the bends."

A basketball player had such long arms
    He could always pull up the score.
If he got home late, he would reach down the chimney
    And easily unlock the door.

A freight train on the C & O
   Is the longest one in the nation.
It takes all summer for it to pass
   Even a single station.

"All the children twelve and under
   Can ride the train free," said Mr. MacLean.
But the line was so long, by the time we got on,
   Most of us were thirteen.

So Cold That . . .

It gets so cold in Siberia
   That the shadows of birds as they fly
Freeze fast to the ground and hold the birds
   Motionless there in the sky.

It gets so cold in Canada
   That all the little dogs
Use their stiffly frozen tails
   To pole-vault over logs.

It gets so cold in Montreal
A bonfire freezes hard.
One fellow sawed a big blaze up
And stacked it in his yard.

For icy months in Canada,
  Until the summer came,
No one could blow a candle out
  Because of the frozen flame.

It gets so cold in northern New Hampshire
   The sunlight freezes on the ground.
This gives the people sunlight at night,
   Which is elsewhere seldom found.

It gets so cold in parts of Vermont
   That on the coldest nights
The candle flames are quickly frozen,
   As are the electric lights.

Down South it's so hot that on some days
   The cows give nothing but steam.
Up North it's so cold that one farmer says
   His cows give only ice cream.

So Fast That . . .

There's a horse in Kentucky so very fast
  He makes the people smile.
In every race he beats his own shadow
  By almost half a mile.

They say that Billy Earthquake,
     Who had his run-ins with the law,
Could stand in front of a mirror
     And beat himself to the draw.

Speedy Fenton shot at a squirrel
     Perched upon a hickory stump,
Then ran so fast to get his prize
     That the bullet hit him in the rump.

Scampering Sam would pitch the ball
     So fast it could not be hit,
Then run to the plate in plenty of time
     To catch it in his mitt.

So Bright

In Boston there lives a boy
  Who is so very bright
His family must wear dark glasses
  To protect themselves from the light.

Polly has a pair of shoes
  That shine so very bright
That when she wears them to a party
  Her host turns out the light.

In London there's a pretty girl
  And so bright is this lucky lass
She can use the palm of either hand
  Instead of a looking glass.

That . . .

There's a girl in New Hampshire whose hair is so red
   That when she goes out at night
The roosters all think the sun is rising
   And crow to welcome the light.

In Florida there are fireflies
    So very big and bright
That children use them to study by
    Almost every night.

In Panama the lightning bugs
    Are so extremely bright
That twenty-five in a goldfish bowl
    Make an excellent street light.

Ben did badly with his bees,
    Despite hard work and thrift,
Till he crossed his bees with lightning bugs
    So some could work the night shift.

If you feed your chickens lightning bugs,
It's likely you will find
They lay electric-light-bulb eggs
Instead of the usual kind.

So Tall That . . .

In Idaho they buy
    The cornstalks from the farmers
And use them for telephone poles
    They're so enormous.

The corn in Oklahoma
   Grows so awfully high
They have to tie it down at night
   To let the moon go by.

So Rocky That . . .

There's a farm in Maine so rocky
   That when the planting is done
You have to find a crack in the ground
   And shoot the seed in with a gun.

So Clear That . . .

In Tennessee there's a lake so clear
   That when you look into it
You can see the Chinese making tea.
   Don't ask me how they do it!

So Steep
That . . .

In Missouri there is a county so steep
   That the goats all have to wear spikes,
And instead of tires the boys all keep
   Big tractor treads on their bikes.

Old Dan Tucker was so tough
   That when he came in from his farm
He always rode a mountain lion
   And carried a bear beneath each arm.

That . . .

Big Jim Hargis spoke so loud
   And looked so fierce when he made a speech
That the wind stopped blowing through the trees
   The waves stopped breaking on the beach.

When Pecos Bill felt a bit reckless
   He'd go out and ride a tornado
Or mount a cyclone down in Texas
   And ride it to Colorado.

The only spill Bill ever got
   Sure left him looking grim.
He had ridden a cyclone down to a trot
   When it rained out from under him.

Bo's beard was so tough
He feared no scorch
When he burned it off
With a big blowtorch.

Fish Stories

Gus caught a fish in Lake Ogee
 That really fought him hard.
It was so large the lake-level fell
 By upwards of a yard.

Up on Silver River
 It's easy to catch the trout.
They jump at the bait so savagely
 They knock themselves plumb out.

Moses Miller caught a bass
 That leaped ten feet, or higher,
Then pulled him along through the water so fast
 It set his boat on fire!

In the Penobscot River
   A perch so big was found
That there was no place in the river
   Where that perch could turn around.

The biggest bass Sam ever caught
   Was as big as the smaller whales.
He fed off the thing for several months
   And roofed his house with the scales.

The biggest catfish ever caught
   Was caught by Big Paul Peach.
He rode the thing, with spurs and all,
   Till it bucked up on the beach.

Tim trained a catfish to live on dry land
   Till at last it followed him around.
But out in a boat with Tim one day,
   The fish fell overboard and drowned.

There's a turtle in Lake Superior,
    And you might not believe this at all,
But every time the monster breathes
    The waters rise and fall.

Tall Troubles

The yellow glasses that William wore
   Were enough to make one frown and mutter,
For William worked in a grocery store
   And couldn't tell lard from butter.

A very absentminded boy
   Used to live in Hackensack.
He'd scratch the pancakes on his plate
   And pour the syrup down his back.

This man had such a difficult name
He'd almost always wreck
At least a dozen pens or so
Whenever he signed a check.

Using an onion for a pincushion
    Is not so very wise.
Sally tried it, but all her needles
    Kept getting tears in their eyes.

Pie-Biter bet that he could bite
    Through pies in a stack of eight,
And he would have won if he hadn't forgot
    To remove a tin pie-plate.

There's a builder on our block
    Who has such romantic dreams
That whenever he builds a house
    He tries to use moonbeams.

Three little girls were very pretty
    And they kept themselves looking simply great,
But their three little brothers got so dirty
    That once they were sold as real estate.

A man once put his dog to bed,
    Then shut *himself* out in the dark.
He didn't discover the error he'd made
    Till he chased a car and couldn't bark.

If you feed a hen on sawdust,
    It's almost sure to wreck her,
And if she hatches one of her eggs,
    Out will come a woodpecker.

Clever Beasts

Dick had a most intelligent dog,
   The smartest in the state.
Whenever Dick picked up his fishing rod,
   His dog dug worms for bait!

From the burning house their dog
   Brought little Nance and Lee,
Then went back in and fetched the fire
   Insurance policy!

Rattlesnakes for watchdogs
   Are good to keep the peace.
They quickly freeze burglars with fear,
   Then rattle for the police.

A man taught his ducks to swim in hot water,
   Which made them squawk and churn their legs.
But the idea worked, as surely it ought 'o,
   For now they lay nothing but hard-boiled eggs.

Old Jed had a burro that minded so well
    That when they fell off a steep mountain top,
Jed hollered "Whoa!" as down they fell,
    And the burro managed to stop!

Woodpeckers peck granite until the sparks fly
    — You can see them on Stony Brook Farm —
Then nimbly they step on the flying sparks
    And keep their feet quite warm.

When the snow gets deep in Idaho,
    Until there comes a thaw,
The cattle drink from deep snow-holes
    By sucking through a straw.

When squirrels are smart they cross the streams
On pieces of bark with sails.
They launch the bark with little screams
And then they hold up their tails.

Clever People

A mighty farmer was L. E. Fant.
   He grew such large potatoes
They had to be sliced with a cross-cut saw,
   As did L. E. Fant's tomatoes.

When the old-time farmers lost their oxen
   They quickly found out how
To yoke up a team of giant bullfrogs
   And use the big jumpers to plow.

When a rattlesnake bit his hoe handle
   It swelled to be so immense
That Squatter Joe split it up
   And made a whole rail fence.

Old John pulls cucumbers right out the field
   And sells them to children for nickels,
For he waters cucumbers with vinegar
   And when they are grown they're pickles.

One hillside farmer, gathering fruit,
   Is such a clever fellow,
He shakes his trees till the fruit rolls down
   And stores itself in the cellar.

Ab Yancey grafted an apple-tree branch
　　On the horns of a big pet deer,
And now from his antlers he gathers red apples
　　Every single year.

When it came to saving money
    McCool didn't miss a trick.
He fed his children jumping beans
    When they asked for a Pogo stick.

A good way for you to keep warm at night
   Is to have your mother spread
A huge pancake just off the stove
   Right over you in bed.

Then in the morning if you wish
   To have your breakfast there
Just nibble off the crispy edge.
   It's good, I do declare!

✳

High wind in Oklahoma
Seldom if ever fails.
The fellows ride it into town,
Using their hats for sails.

The wind in Australia blows so hard,
　　Whipping the ranches by night and day,
That they feed the turkeys bushels of buckshot
　　So they won't be blown away.

　　The fog in Nova Scotia
　　　　That floats round the people's heads
　　Is so thick they pick it and dry it
　　　　And use it for stuffing beds.

There's a tanner who no longer needs
    To use the bark from logs,
Because he's learned to tan his hides
    With the bark of his own dogs.

Hugh has a pair of amazing suspenders
    And each is as good as a wing,
For whenever he comes to a puddle of water
    They lift him right over the thing.

Big Bill once grabbed a bullfrog's leg
When ZOOM! they both were gone,

For the monster jumped clear across the river
With Big Bill hanging on.

And Finally . . .

There's a Lost Canyon way out West,
　　And the people there don't mind it —
Though none of them can ever come back,
　　And nobody else can find it.

They talked of building rubber ships,
　　But "No!" said one debater,
"A fleet of new red rubber ships
　　Might erase the whole equator!"